10 MINUTE
SATs TESTS
READING

AGES 9–10
YEAR 5

KS2

Scholastic Education, an imprint of Scholastic Ltd
Book End, Range Road, Witney, Oxfordshire, OX29 0YD
Registered office: Westfield Road, Southam, Warwickshire CV47 0RA
www.scholastic.co.uk

ISBN 978-1407-17522-5

Printed and bound by Bell and Bain Ltd, Glasgow

Author
Giles Clare

Editorial
Rachel Morgan, Audrey Stokes, Kate Pedlar, Louise Titley

Cover and Series Design
Scholastic Design Team: Nicolle Thomas and Neil Salt

Design
Scholastic Design Team: Alice Duggan

Cover Illustration
Adam Linley @ Beehive Illustration
Visual Generation @ Shutterstock

Illustrations
Rachel Sanson @ The Bright Agency

Acknowledgements
NASA for the use of 'The Mars Rovers: Curiosity' article. Text © NASA, 2016. (NASA Space Place
Program website, 2016); **Bloomsbury Publishing Plc** for the use of extract from *Dragonskin
Slippers* by Jessica Day George, Text © Jessica Day George, 2007 (Bloomsbury Publishing Plc,
2007); **Faber and Faber Ltd** for the use of extract from *The Girl Savage* by Katherine Rundell,
Text © Katherine Rundell, 2011 (Faber and Faber Ltd, 2011); **David Higham Associates** for the
use of 'Quieter Than Snow' by Berlie Doherty from *Walking on Air* by Berlie Doherty. Text © Berlie
Doherty, 1988. (HarperCollins Publishers Ltd, 1993); **United Agents** (www.unitedagents.co.uk)
on behalf of Wendy Cope for the use of 'The Dinosaurs' by Wendy Cope from *Dinosaur Poems*
compiled by Paul Cookson. Text © Wendy Cope, 2015. (Scholastic Ltd, 2015); **Penguin Books
Ltd** for the use of extract from *The Diary of a Wimpy Kid* by Jeff Kinney. Text © Jeff Kinney, 2008.
(Penguin Books Ltd, 2008)

Photographs
page 6: death cap mushroom, syaber/iStock; page 13: Dürer's rhinoceros, nicoolay/iStock;
page 21: geese, Anagramm/iStock; page 29: Mars Rover, freestylephoto/iStock;

Contents

How to use this book

This book contains ten different Reading tests for Year 5, each containing SATs-style questions. As a whole, the complete set of tests provides broad coverage of the test framework for this age group. Each test comprises a text followed by comprehension questions. The texts cover a wide range of subject matter across the three key areas: fiction, non-fiction and poetry.

Some questions require a selected response, where children choose the correct answer from several options. Other questions require a constructed response, where children write a short or extended answer of their own. Guidance on the different question types and the skills needed to deal with them are covered on pages 50 to 61.

A mark scheme and a progress chart are also included towards the end of this book.

Completing the tests

- It is intended that children will take approximately ten minutes to complete each test.

- After your child has completed a test, mark it and together identify and practise any areas where your child is less confident. Ask them to complete the next test at a later date, when you feel they have had enough time to practise and improve.

Protection from danger

The body's defences

Our bodies have many natural ways of protecting themselves from harm. If we hurt ourselves, our nerves pick up the danger signals at once. They send a message to the brain. We feel the pain and take action to stop it.

Eyelashes and eyelids shield our eyes from grit. Nails protect our fingertips and toes. Skin and the vessels that carry blood around our body help to control our temperature. This makes it less likely that we will die from extreme cold or heat.

When we are faced with danger, we need super powers! A gland in our body produces adrenalin. This substance pumps extra oxygen into our blood and makes our heart speed up. It stiffens the muscles. It helps us to concentrate, so that we can fight – or run away fast!

Our protection against illnesses and wounds is called the immune system. Its weapons include white blood cells, which destroy germs. Our bodies can repair themselves and recover from grazes, sprains and even broken bones.

Don't eat these!

We eat many different plants, but some plants are dangerous. This is because they have defences to keep away people and animals. Sharp thorns can tear our skin and stinging hairs can cause a painful rash. The juices of some plants, such as euphorbias, can blister the skin or damage the eyes.

The biggest risk is from plants that have berries, leaves, roots or seeds that are poisonous to eat. They are often mistaken for harmless plants. People may become sick or even die if they eat them. Extremely dangerous plants include hemlock, foxglove and monkshood.

Some fungi, such as mushrooms, are popular foods, but other fungi are deadly.

The one that kills the most people is called the death cap. Its poison causes vomiting and extreme pain, as it attacks the liver and kidneys. It is pale green or yellowish. Young ones are round, but the head grows and flattens to about 5 to 15 centimetres across. People can mistake the death cap for other fungi that are safe to eat.

A dish of death

In 1534 one of the most powerful men in the world, Pope Clement VII, died after eating a death cap mushroom. Was it an accident? Many people believe he was killed by a poisoner.

Extract from *Record Breakers The Most Dangerous* by Philip Steele

Marks

1. What are all nerves connected to?

_____

_____

1

2. Complete this table using words or phrases from the text.

Part of the body	How it protects us
	pick up danger signals and send a message to the brain.
Skin and blood vessels	
	protect our fingertips and toes.
Eyelashes and eyelids	

2

Marks

3. Name **two** ways adrenalin helps us prepare to fight or run away from danger.

1. _____

2. _____

_____

1

4. Look at the sentence: *Our protection against illnesses and wounds is called the immune system.*

Which of the following words is closest in meaning to the word immune?

Tick **one**.

attack ☐

safety ☐

resistance ☐

repair ☐

1

5. Why might it be important to wear gloves when working in the garden? Explain using evidence from the text.

_____

_____

_____

_____

2

10 MINS

Marks

6. The juices of which of these plants or fungi cause skin irritation?

Tick **one**.

death cap mushrooms ☐

euphorbias ☐

hemlock ☐

foxglove ☐

1

7. A mushroom is a type of what?

_____

_____

1

8. Using information from the text, tick **one** box in each row to show whether each statement is **fact** or **opinion**.

	Fact	Opinion
You should never eat berries or nuts you find in the wild.		
Poison has often been used to murder powerful people.		
People sometimes mistake harmful plants and fungi for harmless ones.		
Our bodies protect us from damage and disease on the outside and inside.		

1

Well done! END OF READING TEST 1!

Dragonskin Slippers

Creel has made a deal with a dragon in a cave. She can choose a pair of shoes from his giant collection. While the dragon's back is turned, she spots an unusual blue pair.

I picked them up and went back to the centre of the room, where I had been gathering another group of shoes to try on. I left the blue slippers for last, but I already knew in my gut that they would be the only pair that fitted.

I was right.

None of the boots or sandals, the brogues or even the crude moccasins I thought came from the southlands fitted my feet. They were too big or too small, the toe pinched or the heel did. They were too stiff, or too floppy, for proper walking.

And then I slipped into the blue pair.

They fitted as though they had been made for my feet. They were so light that I felt as if I were barefoot, yet the soles were thick enough that I could not feel the uneven stone floor beneath them. They were supple as I walked and didn't slide or chafe my feet. I had a sudden urge to cut the skirt of my gown off at the knee so that everyone could admire my beautiful new shoes.

"By the Seven Volcanoes!" The brown dragon had returned, and steam was rising from his nostrils as he surveyed my footwear. "What are you doing?"

I was taken aback by his reaction. "You said I could have any pair of shoes that I wanted," I said stubbornly. I had never owned anything as nice as these shoes, and longing for them made me bold. "And these are the only ones that fit me. I want these."

"Any shoes but those!"

I frowned up at him. "No, it was to be any shoes I liked. You never said that there were some pairs I could not have!"

"What's going on?" The voice of the blue-grey came wafting into the shoe cave. "Which shoes did she pick?"

"She picked the – " Theoradus began, roaring back over his winged shoulder to the cave entrance. "She picked the – " Then he looked at me and snapped his fanged muzzle shut.

"You said any pair of shoes," I reminded him. "Or I will stay here, and let my aunt rouse the entire town to come after you." I folded my arms and put my chin in the air. "You gave your word just as I gave mine."

"You don't know what you're doing," the brown dragon said, its eyes narrowed to slits.

Extract from *Dragonskin Slippers* by Jessica Day George

1. **Find** and **copy five** types of shoe that Creel tried on.

Marks

1. _____   4. _____

2. _____   5. _____

3. _____

1

Marks

2. Why do you think Creel tried the blue slippers on last?

_____

_____

_____

1

3. Look at the paragraph beginning: *They fitted as though they had been made for my feet.*

Which word most closely matches the meaning of the word <u>supple</u>?

Tick **one**.

soft ☐   rigid ☐

flexible ☐   delicate ☐

1

4. What is the name of the brown dragon?

_____

_____

1

5. What colour is the second dragon?

_____

1

KEEP IT GOING!

Marks

6. What deal has Creel made with the dragon? She can choose any pair of shoes...

Tick **one**.

and the dragon will let her go. ☐

and she will leave to tell the villagers not to attack the dragon. ☐

or she won't leave and the villagers will attack. ☐

or she will leave and fetch her aunt and villagers to attack. ☐

1

7. Look at the paragraph starting: *"You said any pair of shoes," I reminded him.*

Find and **copy one** word that means the same as <u>stir up</u>.

_____

_____

1

8. How do you think the brown dragon feels about Creel's choice of shoes? Explain your answer using evidence from the text.

_____

_____

_____

_____

3

Well done! END OF READING TEST 2!

The unseen rhino

Imagine drawing a picture of a rhinoceros. Lots of people would find that a challenge. Now imagine drawing a rhino if you had never even seen one! Sounds impossible, right? Well, in 1515, a German artist called Albrecht Dürer made a pretty accurate print of an Indian rhinoceros. The thing was, he had never seen it.

The rhino in question was a present sent from India to the king of Portugal. It arrived by ship in Lisbon in May 1515. The Portuguese king already had a zoo. He wanted to see one of his elephants fight this new beast, but apparently the elephant ran off.

Meanwhile in Germany, Albrecht Dürer heard about the new arrival at the king's zoo. He decided to make a picture of it. As a teenager, Dürer had trained as a goldsmith, but he developed into one of Europe's greatest printmakers. He was interested in science, especially animals and plants, and he loved drawing them too. He made his pictures by drawing onto a smooth block of wood. He then cut away the unwanted wood, leaving the lines of the drawing itself 'in relief'. Finally, he put ink on the block and pressed it onto paper to create a print. He even had to draw the image and write the words back to front so that the picture printed the right way round.

We know that Dürer was successful enough to travel extensively around Europe. However, he didn't go to Portugal to see the rhino. All he had was a brief description of the animal and a quick sketch by an unknown artist. Even so, he made his woodcut and, amazingly, it was fairly close! It certainly looks like an Asian rhino, which live in India and Indonesia.

However, some of the details were wrong: a rhino doesn't have scales on its legs or armoured plates on its flanks and shoulder. Despite this, people in Europe believed Dürer's picture was an accurate representation. Only when other rhinos were brought to Europe 200 years later did people come to see what rhinos really look like.

As for the original rhino, it met an unfortunate end. The king of Portugal sent it to the pope in Rome but, unfortunately, the ship sank on its way to Italy.

Marks

1. What month did the rhinoceros arrive in Lisbon?

_____

_____

1

2. What other animal did the Portuguese king have in his zoo?

_____

_____

1

3. What type of picture was Albrecht Dürer famous for making?

Tick **one**.

paintings ☐

sketches ☐

woodcut prints ☐

engraved prints ☐

1

10 MINS

Marks

4. The lines of Dürer's pictures were *in relief*. What does <u>in relief</u> mean?

_____

_____

1

5. Why was Albrecht Dürer's picture such an impressive feat? Explain using evidence from the text.

_____

_____

_____

_____

_____

2

6. Look at the paragraph beginning: *However, some of the details were wrong...*

Find and **copy one** word that means <u>correct</u>.

_____

1

KEEP IT GOING!

Marks

7. Draw a line to match each person or animal to their country. One has been done for you.

Albrecht Dürer	India
the pope	Portugal
the king	Germany
the rhinoceros	Italy

1

8. Why do you think so few people in Europe had seen animals like rhinos in the 1500s? Use information from the text to help you.

_____

_____

_____

_____

2

Well done! END OF READING TEST 3!

Quieter Than Snow

I went to school a day too soon
And couldn't understand
Why silence hung in the yard like sheets
Nothing to flap or spin, no creaks
or shocks of voices, only air.

And the car park empty of teachers' cars
Only the first September leaves
Dropping like paper.
No racks of bikes
No kicking legs, no fights,
No voices, laughter, anything.

Yet the door was open.
My feet sucked down the corridor.
My reflection walked with me past the hall.
My classroom smelt of nothing

And the silence rolled like thunder in my ears.
At every desk a still child stared at me
Teachers walked through walls and back again
Cupboard doors swung open, and out crept

More silent children, and still more.
They tiptoed round me
Touched me with ice-cold hands
And opened up their mouths with laughter
That was
Quieter than snow.

By Berlie Doherty

Marks

1. Why was nobody else at school when the poet arrived?

_____

_____

1

2. Which month was it?

_____

_____

1

3. The poet describes the leaves as *dropping like paper*. Why?

_____

_____

_____

2

10 MINS

Marks

4. Look at the line: *My feet sucked down the corridor.*

What do you think the poet means by this?

_____

_____

_____

_____

_____

2

5. The poet uses similes to emphasise how quiet it is. **Find** and **copy two** of them.

1. _____

2. _____

1

KEEP IT GOING!

Marks

6. What unusal things does the poet see in the classrooms? Explain how you know, using evidence from the text.

_____

_____

_____

_____

_____

2

7. Thinking about the poem as a whole, how do you think the poet feels?

Tick one.

scared ☐

curious ☐

lonely ☐

annoyed ☐

1

Well done! END OF READING TEST 4!

Test 5
Reading

Amazing migrations

Have you ever seen geese flying in a 'V' formation overhead, or a flock of swallows resting on a telephone line? Have you ever wondered where they are going and why?

These birds are probably heading south for winter in an amazing seasonal migration. Many types of animal migrate. This means that they travel from one place to another. Birds often live in one habitat during one season and then fly to another for the next. For example, swallows arrive in Britain in spring and spend the summer months breeding. They return to their wintering grounds 6000 miles away, back in South Africa, in autumn. Some even cross the Sahara Desert as part of their journey! These tiny birds travel during the day, flying at low altitudes and finding food on the way. As they cross huge hazards like the Sahara, they risk starvation and exhaustion. Amazingly, on average, a migrating swallow can fly at twenty miles an hour for ten hours a day.

But why go to all that effort? It's simple really. Migration is a form of behavioural adaptation – a way of behaving that helps creatures to survive. Animals migrate because they need to find food, a suitable place to breed, and shelter from dangerous weather. If they didn't migrate, they wouldn't be able to survive or reproduce.

It's not just small animals that migrate. Blue whales are the largest animals on the planet and they also migrate. During the summer, they travel up to 3000 miles north or south to the colder waters of the polar regions to feed. Blue whales mostly travel there alone or in small groups.

However, larger groups of whales have been spotted, usually within these colder feeding grounds. In winter, the whales migrate to breed, swimming back towards warmer waters near the equator.

Blue whales eat krill, which are shrimp-like creatures the size of your little finger. A blue whale needs to consume about four tonnes of krill every day. The whale expands its throat and sucks in water and krill. It then filters the water through baleen plates in its mouth and swallows the krill that have been trapped.

Climate change may be affecting the blue whale's food supply and migration patterns. Global warming means that sea temperatures are rising. This means that the krill populations are shrinking north and south closer to the poles. Scientists are concerned that the blue whales will have to migrate even further to reach these food-rich areas. These longer journeys will require more energy and reduce the amount of time the whales spend feeding and building up their strength.

Did you know?

Some monarch butterflies travel an incredible 3000 miles in a year when they migrate. In fact, they spend most of their lifetime migrating and use the Earth's magnetic field to navigate. However, that's nothing compared to tiny Arctic terns, which fly up to 400 miles every day travelling from the Arctic to the Antarctic and back again every year. That's an amazing 45,000 miles in total!

1. What is a migration?

A migration is when animals fly or swim to different places at times of the year.

Marks

1

(1)

2. Where do swallows spend the winter?

Tick **one**.

Britain ☐   South Africa ☑   *They spend the winter in South Africa and the summer in Britian.*

Sahara ☐   South Pole ☐

Marks

① 1

---

3. Look at the sentence: *As they cross huge hazards like the Sahara, they risk starvation and exhaustion.*

Which of the following words is closest in meaning to the word <u>hazards</u>?

Tick **one**.

areas ☐   deserts ☐   *Because the Saharh is hot and dangerous.*

obstacles ☐   dangers ☑

① 1

---

4. Why do some animals migrate? Tick **all** the **correct** statements.

to find a food source ☑   to find somewhere hot ☐

to find somewhere nice to live ☐   to find safety from bad weather ☑

to find a mate ☑   to find their way home ☐

① 1

Marks

5. Complete this table about the blue whale's migration habits.

Region	Sea temperature	Reason the whales go there
polar regions	cold	to feed
equator	warm	to find a mate

 2

2

6. How do monarch butterflies find their way when migrating?

They use the Earth's magnetic field.

 1

1

7. Three types of birds are mentioned in this text. Name all **three**.

1. Artic turn
2. Swallow ✓
3. geese ✓

 1

1

8. Using the text, explain how whale migration is different from swallow migration.

Whale migration is different to swallow migration because swallows fly and whales swim they also go to complety different places.

2

Well done! END OF READING TEST 5!

Red Leaves

Zak hears a strange voice in some woods. He hides behind a tree when he encounters a strange woman called Elder.

He supposed that she could be about his grandma's age when she'd died or older, much, much older even. Her hair hung in a mass of wild frizzy curls down her back and had been dyed flame red. She'd threaded leaves through the top strands like a tangled crown. Zak stared at her clothes. She'd piled one piece on top of the other in an eclectic collection of leaf layers. The overall effect was like the rag rug his mum had once brought home from one of her trips to Africa. It was impossible to tell exactly what the old woman was wearing or how small or large she really was underneath all those petticoats that swept the earth as she walked. Everything she wore seemed to have been chosen to match the russet tones of autumn, like camouflage.

Get a hold of yourself. She's just a homeless old woman. But Zak found that he could not tear his gaze away from her. She was close enough now for him to hear the hollow rumblings of her stomach.

'There, my Crystal, don't you cry. My belly's singing you a lullaby!'

It was then that he realized that she was swaddling a baby wrapped in a crocheted woollen shawl, more holes than blanket. Despite the old woman's hushings, the baby hadn't stirred or made a sound. Zak's heart clamped in his chest. *What's she doing with a baby? Has she stolen it out of someone's pram?*

He was relieved to see a young woman walking her dog up a steep connecting path.

The nearer she drew, the louder the old woman's voice seemed to become.

'But here's a wood wanderer coming. Wafting perfume. Not my kind, gets up my nose. Makes me sneeze.'

The woman held the baby close and rocked it. No movement came from underneath its shawl.

'Here she comes. What do you think, my Crystal? Will she walk right past? Pretend we're invisible? How could anyone not take pity on you, my baby?'

Then she held the bundle up, like an offering. The dog came bounding over and sniffed at it before tossing its head dismissively. The young woman strained to get a closer look, before she too turned and hurried away.

'Could you spare us the price of a cup of tea? No…? Straight past, eyes glazed over, locking us out. Just an old tree stump with gnarly roots. That's all I am these days.'

And with that the old woman dropped the baby on the ground, where it landed with a thud and slid from its blanket. Zak gave a sharp intake of breath and was just about to spring from his hiding place when a bald plastic head rolled in his direction, its blue eyes wide and unblinking.

Extract from *Red Leaves* by Sita Brahmachari

---

1. Read the paragraph beginning *He supposed that.* Look at the sentence: *She'd piled one piece on top of the other in an eclectic collection of leaf layers.*

Which of the following words is closest in meaning to <u>eclectic</u>?

Tick **one**.

Marks

shocking ☐   assorted ☐

weird ☐   similar ☐

1

Marks

2. Find and **copy four** words that the author has used in the paragraph beginning *He supposed that...* to suggest the old woman has a connection with nature.

1. _____

2. _____

3. _____

4. _____

1

3. What is the name of the old woman's baby?

_____

1

4. Who else is in the wood, apart from Zak and the old woman?

_____

1

5. How do you know that the baby is a doll? Give evidence from the text.

_____

_____

_____

1

KEEP IT GOING!

10 MINS

Marks

6. Why might Zak think that the old woman is homeless? Explain your answer with reference to details from the whole text.

_____

_____

_____

_____

_____

_____

3

7. Thinking about what has happened so far, do you think Zak talks to the old woman next? Explain your answer.

Tick **one**.

Yes ☐

No ☐

_____

_____

_____

2

Well done! END OF READING TEST 6!

Test 7
Reading

A curious explorer on Mars

The American space agency NASA has sent lots of spacecraft to explore the Red Planet. In 2012, they successfully landed a large rover on the surface. It has been exploring ever since.

On Earth, where there is water, there are living things. We know that Mars had water a long time ago. But did it also have other conditions life needs?

To find out, NASA sent the Curiosity rover to Mars. Curiosity is the largest robot to ever land on another planet. She is about the size of a small SUV.

Because Curiosity is so big, she also has bigger wheels than the previous rovers. This helps her to roll over rocks and sand without getting stuck. However, even on a long driving day, she still only travels about 660 feet.

Curiosity landed in Gale Crater. This crater is special because it has a tall mountain in the middle. The mountain has many layers of rock. Each layer is made of different minerals from different time periods. These minerals could tell scientists about the history of water on Mars.

The rover uses many scientific instruments to study the rocks in Gale Crater. Curiosity used her drill to make a hole in a rock that once was mud at the bottom of a lake. One of her other instruments studied the powder drilled from the rock. This information helped scientists learn that the Gale Crater had ingredients that ancient life would have needed to survive.

Scientists sent Curiosity to Mars to measure lots of other things, too – including radiation. Radiation is a type of energy that can come from the sun. It travels in high-energy waves that can be harmful to living things. Curiosity found that Mars has high, dangerous levels of radiation.

NASA will use Curiosity's radiation data to design missions to be safer for human explorers.

Curiosity brought 17 cameras with her to the Red Planet – more than any other rover. She uses some of her cameras to take photos of her journey. Cameras also act as Curiosity's eyes, helping her to spot and stay away from danger.

One of Curiosity's cameras – at the end of her 7 foot long robotic arm – even acts like a sort of 'selfie stick'. She can hold the camera two metres away and take a selfie to send back to Earth!

Extract from 'The Mars Rovers: Curiosity' article by NASA

Marks

1. What is another name for Mars?

_____

_____

1

2. What did we already know existed on Mars a long time ago before NASA sent Curiosity to explore?

Tick **one**.

water ☐   mud ☐

radiation ☐   minerals ☐

1

3. Curiosity is described as **two** things beginning with the letter 'r'. **Find** and **copy** them both.

1. _____

2. _____

1

Marks

4. What is special about the mountain in Gale Crater?

_____

_____

_____

_____

2

5. What life-threatening hazard did Curiosity discover humans would face on Mars?

_____

_____

1

6. Draw lines to match each set of jumbled phrases to make the correct sentences.

Curiosity has large wheels	to study the rocks	for signs of ancient life.
Curiosity has cameras	to send back pictures	without getting stuck.
Curiosity has instruments	to roll over rocks	of its environment.

2

7. Has Curiosity found evidence that there used to be life on Mars? Explain your answer, referring to the text.

_____

_____

_____

2

Well done! END OF READING TEST 7!

The Dinosaurs

They lived on our planet before there were people,
Forebears of our reptiles and fishes and birds,
They were not called dinosaurs then – they were nameless.
They lived on our planet before there were words.

Some were as tall as a four-storey building.
To keep themselves going, they needed to munch
The green things around them from dawn until twilight –
Their waking existence was just one long lunch.

Some preferred flesh. They would tear at their dinner
With terrible fingers and teeth sharp as knives.
Others grew horns, massive spikes, bony armour,
To ward off the carnivores, safeguard their lives.

They all disappeared and the world went on turning.
We humans evolved, with our language, our games,
Our hunger for knowledge. We found the lost creatures.
We dug up their bones and we gave them their names.

They stand in museums; grand skeletons, relics
Exhumed after millions of years in the ground.
And we are still learning. Who knows what strange monsters
Lie buried around us and wait to be found?

By Wendy Cope

Marks

1. The dinosaurs are described as *Forebears of our reptiles and fishes and birds.*

Which word is closest in meaning to the word <u>forebears</u>?

Tick **one.**

children ☐

descendants ☐

parents ☐

ancestors ☐

1

2. Read the **second** line and the **fourth** line of each verse. What do you notice?

_____

_____

_____

1

3. Look at the verse containing the line: *Their waking existence was just one long lunch.*

Why did some dinosaurs need to eat all day?

_____

_____

_____

2

Marks

4. Name **three** body parts some dinosaurs used to protect themselves.

1. _____

2. _____

3. _____

1

5. Find and **copy** the word used to describe dinosaurs that ate other dinosaurs.

_____

_____

1

6. The author compares how dinosaurs and humans behave. How are their behaviours different? Give some examples from the text.

_____

_____

_____

_____

2

KEEP IT GOING!

Marks

7. What part of the dinosaurs do we display in museums?

_____

_____

1

8. How would you summarise the main theme of this poem?

Tick **one**.

We have made lots of amazing discoveries
about dinosaurs. ☐

We will probably find out lots more about
dinosaurs in the future ☐

We know that there were lots
of different dinosaurs. ☐

We have learned lots and will always
want to learn more from history. ☐

1

Well done! END OF READING TEST 8!

The Girl Savage

Wilhelmina (Will) lives on a farm in Africa. She is preparing a fire with her friend, Simon, and her monkey, Kezia.

Will was good at lighting fires. She was proud of it. Because fire was such an odd thing – it was like water, she reckoned; if we didn't have the name for it, didn't have it every day, we'd be so choked and laughing and flabbergasted by it. Will tried to teach Simon this strange-wonder, but it wasn't really a success.

'No, but *look*. Look properly.' She blew on the flames, and she jabbed Simon with a twig. '*Look*, Si. Like it's alive and it's also-not-really-alive. Watch: it moves without wind. D'you see?' She blew harder, and sparks shot into the air. 'It *is* amazing, isn't it, Si?'

'Ja. I guess. It is.' Simon looked unconvinced. He wished it would heat up faster. They had lit the fire at the foot of the tree house, which meant there was no breeze to help it along but had the great advantage that they knew they couldn't be disturbed. When they were younger, they had done their cooking in the bread-smelling kitchen, but then the two of them had set fire to the wall (Simon said it was Will's fault: Will said it was both of them) frying bantam eggs in oil that was too spitting-hot. The wall was still stained black, and Will still made her ashamed-smiling face whenever she passed it.

Since then, Will had had to bake her food in open fires, or in the hollows of the tree roots, which was nicer anyway; she could make meals that tasted enticingly of smoke and leaves, and eggs and animal, and Africa.

Simon stretched, and snuffed at the smoke. 'It's ready now, ja.'

'You've got no patience, Si,' said Will; and that was rich, thought Simon, because she had even less. 'It needs more wood, hey, it's still hungry.'

'Ja. But more's to the point. *I'm* still hungry. It *is* ready. 'Ts just you're blind like a chungololo … *Ow!*'

Will had picked up a gooseberry from the pile at her side and flicked it at Simon's head.

'Hey! That's my eye, mad girl.' He flicked one back from his own pile and Will caught it in her mouth – 'ha-*ha!*' – and inside she burned and whooped with pleasure. *That* was how life should be: snap-gulp-whoop. She grinned, with yellow gooseberry seeds between her teeth. 'Ja, OK. You win. Fire's ready.'

Together they split open the banana skins with shards of sharp flint. Kezia chattered and tugged at the bunch in Will's hand. After only a week, Will had trained her to sleep inside her shirt, and to sit on her shoulder and chew at her hair. The bananas today were the best on the farm, in celebration of Kezia's cleverness.

Extract from *The Girl Savage* by Katherine Rundell

1. Through the character of Will, the author makes an unusual comparison between fire and what substance?

Marks

_____

_____

1

2. Why do you think Simon wishes the fire would heat up faster?

_____

_____

1

3. What caused the fire in the kitchen?

_____

1

Marks

4. Look at the sentence: *The wall was still stained black, and Will still made her ashamed-smiling face whenever she passed it.*

What does this tell you about how Will feels about the fire?

_____

_____

_____

_____

2

5. Simon tells Will: *'Ts just you're blind like a chungololo.*

What do you think a *chungololo* might be?

_____

_____

1

6. Simon describes Will as a *mad girl*. Give **two** examples of Will's behaviour that show that she is a wild type of person.

1. _____

_____

2. _____

_____

2

KEEP IT GOING!

7. What are Will and Simon baking on the fire?

_____

_____

Marks

1

8. In general, what do you think Will likes best about her life on an African farm?

Tick one.

She can have fun with her friend, Simon. ☐

She is mostly free to do whatever she wants. ☐

She loves making and cooking on fires. ☐

She knows how to look after herself. ☐

1

Well done! END OF READING TEST 9!

Jeff Kinney Q&A

Jeff Kinney is author of the hugely popular Wimpy Kid *books.*

Describe *Diary of a Wimpy Kid*.

Diary of a Wimpy Kid is the fulfilment of a life-long dream. I had always wanted to be a cartoonist, but I found that it was very tough to break into the world of newspaper syndication. So I started playing with a style that mixed cartoons and 'traditional' writing, and that's how *Diary of a Wimpy Kid* was born. The book centres around a middle-school student named Greg Heffley, who thinks very highly of himself, but is oblivious to his own imperfections.

What is your favourite family story?

When I was eight or nine, my older brother, Scott, played a practical joke on me. On the first night of summer vacation, Scott woke me up in the middle of the night. He was dressed in his school clothes and was wearing his backpack. He told me that I had slept through the whole summer, and I had even missed our family's trip to Disney World. Then, he told me that luckily, I had woken up in time for the first day of school. So I got dressed for school, went downstairs, and made myself breakfast. I don't know how long it took me to figure out it was 2.00 in the morning. I've got this story in my book.

Describe your most memorable teacher.

My most memorable teacher was named Mrs Norton. She was quite a bit older than the other teachers in my elementary school, and not, from

outward appearances, the type of person you'd expect might place a high value on humour. But Mrs Norton encouraged her fifth-graders to try to be funny. There was one kid named James who stayed quiet the whole school year and, on the last day of class, Mrs Norton invited James to do anything he wanted for five minutes. Without hesitation, James jumped up on a desk and did a spot-on impersonation of Charlie Chaplin, including a soft-shoe routine. Mrs Norton could always bring out the best in kids, and she brought me out of my shell, too.

Why do you write books for kids?

I write for kids because I think the most interesting (and most humorous) stories come from people's childhoods. When I was writing *Diary of a Wimpy Kid*, I had a blast talking on the phone to my younger brother, Patrick, remembering all of the things that happened to our family when we were growing up. I think if everyone would write down the funny stories from their own childhoods, the world would be a better place.

How do you come up with the names for your characters?

I usually pick by the sound of it. Rowley is not really a regular kid's name; it is a town in Massachusetts.

Is Greg a good role model?

No. In fact, you should do the opposite of everything Greg does.

Extract from *Diary of a Wimpy Kid* by Jeff Kinney

1. Before he became an author, what did Jeff Kinney want to be?

_____

Marks

KEEP IT GOING!

1

Marks

2. The main character in Jeff's books *is oblivious to his own imperfections.* Tick the phrase below that you think means the same as this:

Tick **one**.

He can't see his own faults. ☐

He makes obvious mistakes. ☐

He isn't perfect. ☐

He won't admit when he is wrong. ☐

1

3. Jeff's brother, Scott, woke him up in the middle of the night and told him **three** lies. What were they?

1. _____

2. _____

3. _____

2

4. What positive effect did Jeff's teacher have on him? Find evidence in the text and explain what it means.

_____

_____

_____

2

Marks

5. How does Jeff come up with ideas for his stories and characters?

_____

_____

_____

_____

2

6. This type of text is known as a 'Q&A'. What do you think 'Q&A' stands for?

_____

1

7. Does Jeff think that his character, Greg, is a good role model?

Tick **one**.

Yes, Jeff thinks that Greg always
does the right thing. ☐

No, Jeff thinks you should do the
opposite of everything Greg does. ☐

Yes, because Greg is based on
Jeff's childhood. ☐

No, because Greg is based on
Jeff's brother. ☐

1

Well done! END OF READING TEST 10!

Answers
Reading

Q	Mark scheme for Reading Test 1: Protection from danger	Marks
1	**Award 1 mark** for: the brain	1
2	**Award 2 marks** for all four correct answers: | Part of the body	How it protects us
---	---
Nerves	pick up danger signals and send a message to the brain.
Skin and blood vessels	**carry blood around our body (to help control our temperature).**
Nails	protect our fingertips and toes.
Eyelashes and eyelids	**shield our eyes from grit.** | **Award 1 mark** for two or three correct answers.	2
3	**Award 1 mark** each for any two of the following: • pumps extra oxygen • makes our heart speed up • stiffens muscles • helps us concentrate	1
4	**Award 1 mark** for: resistance	1
5	**Award 2 marks** for an answer that refers to two injuries and their causes, such as: You might cut your hand on a thorn or get a rash from the stinging hairs of some plants. **Award 1 mark** for an answer referring to one injury with its cause, such as: You might get a blister on your skin from a plant's juices. OR for an answer referring to two potential injuries but without their causes, such as: You might get a tear in your skin or a rash on your arm.	2
6	**Award 1 mark** for: euphorbias	1
7	**Award 1 mark** for: fungus (or fungi)	1
8	**Award 1 mark** for all four correct: opinion, opinion, fact, fact	1
	Total	10

Q	Mark scheme for Reading Test 2: Dragonskin Slippers	Marks
1	**Award 1 mark** for all correct: boots, sandals, brogues, moccasins, slippers	1
2	**Award 1 mark** for an answer that indicates she wanted to leave the best until last, such as: She knew she would like them and she was teasing herself by trying on the others first.	1
3	**Award 1 mark** for: flexible	1
4	**Award 1 mark** for: Theoradus	1
5	**Award 1 mark** for: blue-grey	1
6	**Award 1 mark** for: or she won't leave and the villagers will attack.	1
7	**Award 1 mark** for: rouse	1

Q	Mark scheme for Reading Test 2: Dragonskin Slippers	Marks
8	**Award 3 marks** for an answer that refers to how the dragon seems shocked, frustrated and angry, each illustrated by evidence from the text. For example: Theoradus is shocked at first when he shouts, "By the Seven Volcanoes!" He is also frustrated because Creel has chosen the one pair of shoes he didn't want her to pick, as shown when he says "Any shoes but those!" He also seems very angry because he can't even manage to say out loud what she's chosen to the other dragon. **Award 2 marks** for two of the above. **Award I mark** for one of the above.	3
	Total	10

Q	Mark scheme for Reading Test 3: The Unseen Rhino	Marks
1	**Award I mark** for: May	1
2	**Award I mark** for: elephants	1
3	**Award I mark** for: woodcut prints	1
4	**Award I mark** for an answer that indicates the lines are raised higher than the rest of the wood, such as: The lines actually stick out because the rest of the wood has been cut away.	1
5	**Award 2 marks** for an answer that refers to how he had not seen a rhino and what he based his picture on. For example: He had never actually been to see the real rhino in Portugal. He made his picture from just a description and a quick sketch by a different artist. **Award I mark** for an answer referring to one of the above only.	2
6	**Award I mark** for: accurate	1
7	**Award I mark** for all correct: Albrecht Dürer → Germany the pope → Italy the king → Portugal the rhinoceros → India	1
8	**Award 2 marks** for an answer that refers to how difficult or expensive it was to travel and how risky it was to transport such animals. For example: Not many people could travel so far to see them because it was expensive/took a long time to travel by boat. Also, there weren't many animals to see because it was hard to bring them to Europe as the ships might sink. **Award I mark** for an answer referring to one of the above only.	2
	Total	10

Q	Mark scheme for Reading Test 4: Quieter Than Snow	Marks
1	**Award I mark** for: The poet went a day too soon.	1
2	**Award I mark** for: September	1
3	**Award 2 marks** for an answer that refers to the season **and** a similarity between falling leaves and dropping paper such as: The leaves are falling because it is autumn and they are crisp like paper/they fall silently like paper/they float down gently like paper. **Award I mark** for an answer referring to a similar appearance/sound/movement of falling leaves and dropping paper but not the season. Do not award a mark for a reference only to the season, such as: Because it's autumn.	2
4	**Award 2 marks** for an answer that refers to the double meaning of 'sucked' in this context. For example: It could mean the poet's shoes made a sucking noise on the floor or it could mean the poet couldn't help it, like they were being sucked into the school against their will. **Award I mark** for an answer referring to one of the meanings of 'sucked' only.	2

Q	Mark scheme for Reading Test 4: Quieter Than Snow	Marks
5	**Award 1 mark** for: • silence hung in the yard like sheets • silence rolled like thunder in my ears	1
6	**Award 2 marks** for an answer that refers to ghosts with two pieces of appropriate evidence from the text. For example: There are ghosts because the teachers could walk through walls and when the children laughed there was no sound. Also accept an answer that suggests the poet imagines seeing ghosts, rather than actually seeing them – with the appropriate evidence as explained above. **Award 1 mark** for an answer referring to ghosts with one piece of appropriate evidence for the text. For example: The poet sees some children who are ghosts because their hands are 'ice-cold'.	2
7	**Award 1 mark** for: curious	1
	Total	10

Q	Mark scheme for Reading Test 5: Amazing migration	Marks
1	**Award 1 mark** for: It's when animals move from one place to another.	1
2	**Award 1 mark** for: South Africa	1
3	**Award 1 mark** for: dangers	1
4	**Award 1 mark** for all of the following correctly ticked: to find a food source; to find safety for bad weather; to find a mate.	2
5	**Award 2 marks** for all five correct answers: <table><tr><td>Region</td><td>Sea temperature</td><td>Reason the whales go there</td></tr><tr><td>polar regions</td><td>colder water</td><td>to eat/feed</td></tr><tr><td>near the equator</td><td>warmer water</td><td>to breed</td></tr></table> **Award 1 mark** for any four answers correct.	1
6	**Award 1 mark** for: They use the Earth's magnetic field to navigate.	1
7	**Award 1 mark** for all three correct: 1. geese 2. swallows 3. terns	1
8	**Award 2 marks** for an answer that refers to the differences in distance and climate. For example: The swallows migrate further than whales and they travel to cold places to breed, but the whales migrate to warmer waters. **Award 1 mark** for one correct answer. Do not accept simple comparisons, such as: • Whales swim whereas swallows fly. • Whales go by sea and swallows go over deserts.	2
	Total	10

Q	Mark scheme for Reading Test 6: Red Leaves	Marks
1	**Award 1 mark** for: assorted	1
2	**Award 1 mark** for any four of the following: *wild, flame, leaf or leaves, earth, russet, autumn, camouflage*	1
3	**Award 1 mark** for: Crystal	1
4	**Award 1 mark** for: a young woman (walking her dog)	1
5	**Award 1 mark** for: When it falls on the ground, Zak sees its bald plastic head, which means it's a doll not a baby.	1

Q	Mark scheme for Reading Test 6: Red Leaves	Marks
6	**Award 3 marks** for an answer that refers to three specific details taken from different paragraphs as evidence for her homelessness. For example: The old woman is wearing lots of clothes on top of each other to keep her warm. Zak can hear her stomach rumbling because she is hungry. She also complains that people won't even give her money for a cup of tea, so she probably doesn't have any money and may have been begging. **Award 2 marks** for an answer with two specific details. **Award 1 mark** for only one specific detail.	3
7	**Award 2 marks** for either yes or no with a full explanation based on details from the text. For example: • Yes. I think Zak will feel sorry for her as everyone else ignores her and she has a pretend baby. • No. Zak will keep hiding behind the tree as the woman seems strange talking to herself and her doll and he will hurry away like the others. **Award 1 mark** for an answer with relevant explanations that do not directly reference details from the text, such as: Yes. Zak probably thinks it's a shame the woman hasn't got any friends.	2
	Total	10

Q	Mark scheme for Reading Test 7: A curious explorer on Mars	Marks
1	**Award 1 mark** for: the Red Planet	1
2	**Award 1 mark** for: water	1
3	**Award 1 mark** for both correct: 1. rover 2. robot	1
4	**Award 2 marks** for an answer that refers to the different layers of rock/minerals and what they can reveal to scientists, such as: The mountain is made of lots of different layers of rock that scientists can study to find out about the history of water on Mars. **Award 1 mark** for an answer that refers to only one of these elements, such as: Scientists can study it to see if there was water on Mars.	2
5	**Award 1 mark** for: high/dangerous levels of radiation	1
6	**Award 2 marks** for all three sets of phrases correctly matched: Curiosity has large wheels → to roll over rocks → without getting stuck. Curiosity has cameras → to send back pictures → of its environment. Curiosity has instruments → to study the rocks → for signs of ancient life. **Award 1 mark** for three sets of phrases partially matched correctly.	2
7	**Award 2 marks** for an answer that explains that the rover has not provided proof that life existed but that it has shown that the correct conditions for life existed. For example: No, Curiosity hasn't found evidence of life, but it did discover that the Gale Crater had the ingredients which ancient life would have needed to survive. **Award 1 mark** for an answer that refers to the lack of proof without further explanation.	2
	Total	10

Q	Mark scheme for Reading Test 8: The Dinosaurs	Marks
1	**Award 1 mark** for: ancestors	1
2	**Award 1 mark** for an answer that refers to the second and fourth line of each verse rhyming: birds/words, munch/lunch, knives/lives, games/names, ground/found	1
3	**Award 2 marks** for an answer that refers to the large size of the dinosaurs and to the low amount of energy from a herbivore diet. For example: They needed to eat all day because they were as big as a four-storey house. Also, these dinosaurs ate leaves, which don't contain much energy, so they had to eat a lot of them. **Award 1 mark** for an answer that refers to only one of the reasons above.	2

Q	Mark scheme for Reading Test 8: The Dinosaurs	Marks
4	**Award 1 mark** for all three correct: 1. horns 2. (massive) spikes 3. armour	1
5	**Award 1 mark** for: carnivores	1
6	**Award 2 marks** for an answer that contrasts the eating, hunting or fighting habits of the dinosaurs with the peaceful, knowledge-seeking behaviour of humans. For example: The poet shows that the dinosaurs spent most of their time hunting or fighting each other, but humans have a hunger for knowledge and have spent lots of time discovering things and inventing language. **Award 1 mark** for an answer that contrasts the behaviour in the same way but without examples from the text. For example: The dinosaurs seem to be violent and the humans seem to do more peaceful things.	2
7	**Award 1 mark** for: their skeletons/bones	1
8	**Award 1 mark** for: We have learned lots and will always want to learn more from history.	1
	Total	10

Q	Mark scheme for Reading Test 9: The Girl Savage	Marks
1	**Award 1 mark** for: water	1
2	**Award 1 mark** for: He is hungry.	1
3	**Award 1 mark** for: (spitting-hot) oil	1
4	**Award 2 marks** for an answer that explains that Will seems to be both embarrassed and pleased with the mess they made. For example: Will is embarrassed about the mess the fire made but she is also secretly quite pleased for causing so much trouble. **Award 1 mark** for an answer that gives one example, such as: She seems to be embarrassed that they caused a fire.	2
5	**Award 1 mark** for: a type of animal (a chungololo is an African word meaning 'millipede'; some scientists believe that millipedes are blind so there is a similarity with the saying 'as blind as a bat')	1
6	**Award 2 marks** each for any two examples, such as: • Will prefers cooking on open fires or in tree roots rather than the kitchen. • She lets her monkey sleep in her shirt and chew her hair. • She throws her gooseberries at her friend and whoops with pleasure when she catches one in her mouth. **Award 1 mark** for one example.	2
7	**Award 1 mark** for: bananas	1
8	**Award 1 mark** for: She is mostly free to do whatever she wants.	1
	Total	10

Q	Mark scheme for Reading Test 10: Jeff Kinney Q&A	Marks
1	**Award 1 mark** for: a cartoonist	1
2	**Award 1 mark** for: He can't see his own faults.	1
3	**Award 2 marks** for all three correct answers: 1. He had slept through the whole summer. 2. He had missed the trip to Disney World. 3. It was the first day of school. **Award 1 mark** for any two of the above.	2

Q	Mark scheme for Reading Test 10: Jeff Kinney Q&A	Marks
4	**Award 2 marks** for an answer that refers to how his teacher brought him out of his shell and its meaning. For example: Mrs Norton brought Jeff out of his shell, which means that she helped him feel more confident. **Award 1 mark** for an answer referring to how she brought him out of his shell without explaining what this means. Do not accept reference to bringing the best out of him or encouraging him to be funny.	2
5	**Award 2 marks** for an answer that refers to how Jeff uses his own funny childhood experiences and how he uses sounds he likes. For example: Jeff talks to his younger brother about funny stories from when they were young and he chooses names he likes the sounds of, like Rowley. **Award 1 mark** for an answer referring to either his childhood experiences or how he chooses names by sounds.	2
6	**Award 1 mark** for: Question and Answer	1
7	**Award 1 mark** for: No, Jeff thinks you should do the opposite of everything Greg does.	1
	Total	10

Skills check

Question type 1

Explain the meaning of words

What to expect

Some questions ask you to think about the meaning of certain words. The word is likely to be unfamiliar or it may have more than one meaning. You will need to look at the word in context. This means you will have to consider the words that come before and after to help you understand the word's meaning. Don't just guess. The context will provide the clues.

Example

Alexa was really excited. Her favourite author had just posted some amazing news on social media. After a three-year wait, there was going to be a brand new *Barry Spotter* novel in the autumn. But when Alexa read more about it, she frowned: there would be no book to buy. Instead, the author was taking the novel approach of publishing the story chapter-by-chapter on a website. Alexa thought that sounded weird.

1. Look at the paragraph beginning *Alexa was really excited...*

Which word most closely matches the meaning of the word <u>unusual</u>?

Tick **one**.

amazing	☐
novel	✔
social	☐
weird	☐

1 mark

Explanation: Although *weird* can mean *unusual*, the word that most closely matches the meaning of *unusual* is *novel*. The word *novel* occurs twice in the paragraph: as a noun meaning a story book; and as an adjective meaning unusual. The context provides the clues: Alexa's reaction is to frown because *there would be no book to buy*, which sounds *weird* to her, suggesting there is something unusual about how the story is going to be published (*chapter-by-chapter on a website*).

Question type 2

Find and record information

What to expect

Some questions ask you to find a particular piece of information or identify key details in a piece of fiction or non-fiction. You will need to scan the text to quickly find a word or phrase. You will often be expected to copy out the information word for word from the text.

Example

Brushing your teeth regularly is very important. Firstly, it helps prevent tooth decay. Even though your teeth are very hard on the outside, they can become damaged, which leads to painful toothache. Another reason to brush your teeth twice a day is to prevent gum disease. Gingivitis is a painful inflammation of the gums where they meet your teeth. Both tooth decay and gum disease are caused by plaque, which is a build-up of food and bacteria in the mouth.

1. What are the two main reasons to brush your teeth? **Find** and **copy two** phrases from the text.

1. *it helps prevent tooth decay*

2. *it helps prevent gum disease*

1 mark

Explanation: The two main reasons are given at separate points within the paragraph. The key to answering this question is to recognise that the word *prevent* introduces both reasons. The rest of the information in the paragraph explains more about the two reasons given and shouldn't be used to answer the question. For example, *painful toothache* would not be acceptable as the copied phrase does not mention how brushing *prevents* it.

Skills check

Question type 3
Summarise the main ideas

What to expect

Some questions ask you to identify the main point or message from a number of paragraphs or the text as a whole. You will not need to write a summary yourself, but choose from some likely options. You may need to skim read the text again to get an overall grasp of how to answer the question.

Example

What you eat affects how you feel today, but will also affect your future. Good nutrition is essential to leading a healthy lifestyle. Along with regular exercise, a healthy diet can keep you well today and reduce the risk of dangerous diseases as you get older. There are lots of ways to eat healthily: eat lots of fresh fruit and veg; try whole-grain cereals; switch to low-fat milk; choose lean protein; cut back on fatty, processed food; and drink water instead of sugary drinks. It's easier than you think if you take small steps each week to improve your nutrition today and to protect you from problems in the years to come.

1. Thinking about the text as a whole, what is the main message?

Tick **one**.

Fatty foods should be cut back as part of a healthy diet. ☐

Regular exercise is an important part of leading a healthy lifestyle. ☐

Dangerous diseases are caused by a poor diet. ☐

Improving your diet will make you healthier now and in the future. ✔

1 mark

Explanation: All four of the choices contain correct information. However, only the final option summarises a point which is made a number of times in the paragraph (your diet affects your health now and in the future). The other options concentrate too narrowly on more specific ideas and not this main message.

Skills check

Question type 4

Make inferences

What to expect

Some questions ask you to 'read between the lines'. In other words, the meaning of a piece of writing may not be completely obvious. Sometimes you will need to work out what the writer means from clues in the text. This is called making an inference. You may also be asked to justify your reasons for making the inference by using evidence from the text.

Example

Caleb and his brother Freddie were in New York. In Midtown Manhattan, the Empire State Building towered over them. Caleb smiled. It was taller and more magnificent that he had imagined. He turned to his brother. "Well, what are we waiting for?" he asked. "There's no queue. We can take a lift straight to the top."

Freddie glanced up at the skyscraper. It seemed to go on up and up forever. He gulped and felt his legs shake unsteadily beneath him. "I think we should go to Central Park first," he replied. "It will be dark soon otherwise. We can come back here another day."

1. What evidence is there that Freddie doesn't like heights?

He doesn't like heights because he seems scared. He swallows nervously and feels a bit shaky. He also makes an excuse that they should go to a different place because he is trying to put off going to the top of the building.

2 marks

Explanation: The writer never says that *Freddie was scared of heights*. However, the clues are there in the text. Reading between the lines, you can make the inference that his nervous behaviour and his excuse indicate that he does not like heights. To achieve both marks, you would need to mention both his nervousness and his excuse as evidence.

Question type 5
Make predictions

What to expect

Some questions ask you to explain what you think will happen next. This is called making a prediction. Like making an inference, you should always make your prediction based on evidence from the text. Don't guess. Use what's happened already to make a reasoned decision about what happens next.

Example

Ella raised her hands confidently to the piano keyboard. This was her moment. Her chance to shine. As always, she had practised for hour after hour. She knew the piece inside out: her fingers would take over and skittle up and down the black and white keys almost with a mind of their own. Ella allowed herself a glance at the audience. It was a mistake. She caught a glimpse of her mum, who gave her a tense smile. Over her mother's shoulder, Ella spotted the long table at which sat the three stony-faced, silent judges. The butterflies took flight in Ella's stomach. She glanced back down at her hands and noticed that her fingers were trembling slightly.

1. What does this paragraph suggest might happen next?

It suggests that Ella will not perform her piano piece well because she made the mistake of looking at the judges and losing her confidence.

2 marks

Explanation: Making a prediction often involves making inferences too. Here you can infer that Ella's nerves are triggered by seeing the judges. The writer calls this a mistake. You can infer from this that things are not going to go as planned in the performance. To achieve both marks, you would need to mention how her mistake (looking at the judges) might affect her performance.

Skills check

Question type 6

Show how language, structure and presentation add to meaning

What to expect

Some questions ask you to identify how the author's choice of language, structure and presentation make the meaning of the whole text clear. You might need to show how a story is structured or find key moments that affect the overall meaning. You might be asked how particular words or phrases make the meaning clearer.

Example

> Roxanne wiped a bead of sweat from the corner of her eye. The sun was beating down steadily. As Roxanne crossed the park, the still summer air stirred lazily. For a moment, a soothing breeze brushed gently across her hot face. The leaves in the trees fluttered briefly but came to rest again. It reminded Roxanne of a sleepy cat stretching for a moment before returning to its peaceful slumber.

1. **Find** and **copy four** words or phrases from the paragraph that suggest a calm scene.

1. _still_

2. _soothing_

3. _sleepy_

4. _peaceful_

2 marks

Explanation: Any four of: still, stirred lazily, soothing (breeze), (brushed) gently, fluttering briefly, came to rest, sleepy, peaceful (slumber) would be acceptable. All of the words and phrases listed are used by the author to 'paint a picture' of a hot, peaceful summer's day in a park where a breeze briefly disturbs the calm scene.

Skills check

Question type 7

Explain how certain words and phrases enhance meaning

What to expect

Some questions ask you to look closely at the author's choice of language. You might be asked how particular words or phrases create atmosphere, or make an image more vivid or easier to imagine. These questions can be quite similar to question type 6, but you will be asked to give your own impressions and to interpret the text more deeply.

Example

Roxanne wiped a bead of sweat from the corner of her eye. The sun was beating down steadily. As Roxanne crossed the park, the still summer air stirred lazily. For a moment, a soothing breeze brushed gently across her hot face. The leaves in the trees fluttered briefly but came to rest again. It reminded Roxanne of a sleepy cat stretching for a moment before returning to its peaceful slumber.

I. What does the following phrase tell you about the kind of day it is in the story?
a sleepy cat stretching for a moment before returning to its peaceful slumber

It shows what a hot, restful kind of day it is: like a lazy cat that can't
be bothered to move, apart from to stretch, even the leaves on the
trees can hardly move.

2 marks

Explanation: This simile is used by the author to 'paint a picture' of a hot, peaceful summer's day in a park where a short breeze is the only movement. To be awarded both marks, you would be expected to identify the effect of the language, and give an explanation as to why you think this.

Question type 8
Making comparisons

Can you...

● make comparisons to show how things are similar or different in a text?

What you need to know

● 'Comparing' means showing how things are different and how they are similar.
● You may be asked to compare characters, places, opinions or ideas.
● You may have to compare ideas from different paragraphs, or across the whole text.
● You may have to write some sentences of your own. Useful words to use when comparing things are: whereas, however, in contrast, on the other hand, in comparison.
● In a full-length test, there will not be more than three comparison questions.

Example

> Yesterday, I drove past a house I used to live in many years ago. It looked very different from when I used to live there. Although nothing has been added to the building (no extensions or loft conversions), the outside has been painted pale blue and there are new windows and doors. The garden doesn't look as tidy as it used to though! All the trees are overgrown and the new owners have replaced my favourite flowerbed with tarmac.

1. What is the same today as when the writer lived there?

The size and shape of the building – nothing has been added.

2. Give **two** ways in which the garden is not as nice as it used to be.

1. _The trees are overgrown._

2. _The writer's favourite flowerbed is now tarmac_

Skills check

Question type 9
Fact and opinion

Can you...

- tell the difference between a fact and an opinion?

What you need to know

- A fact is true and can be proved.
- An opinion is something that someone thinks or believes. It is possible for two people to have different opinions about something.
- Sometimes opinions are written so they look like facts. Watch out for phrases such as 'Everybody knows...' and 'There can be no doubt...'.

Example

Everybody knows that chocolate cake is the best kind of cake. It's so delicious that most supermarkets sell it. My recipe for chocolate cake contains dark chocolate, cream and sugar, which is why it is the best chocolate cake ever!

1. Put a tick in the correct box to show whether each of the following statements is a fact or an opinion.

	Fact	Opinion
Chocolate cake is the best kind of cake.		✓
Most supermarkets sell chocolate cake.	✓	
The writer's recipe for chocolate cake contains dark chocolate, cream and sugar.	✓	

You need all three ticks for one mark. Watch out for the opinion beginning 'Everybody knows...', which makes the sentence look like a fact. However, chocolate cake cannot be proved to be the best: this is just what the writer thinks.